The Penguin in the Fridge

and other cool poems

by Peter Dixon

Illustrated by David Thomas

MACMILLAN CHILDREN'S BOOKS

First published 2001
by Macmillan Children's Books
a division of Macmillan Publishers Ltd
25 Eccleston Place, London SW1W 9NF
Basingstoke and Oxford
www.macmillan.com

Associated companies throughout the world

ISBN 0 330 48019 7

1 3 5 7 9 8 6 4 2

A CIP catalogue record for this book is available from the British Library.

Printed by Mackays of Chatham plc, Chatham, Kent.

Contents

The Penguin in the Fridge

Deep within the refrigerator
in the space once occupied
by Grandma's gammon steak
a penguin has built a small nest
(chips and cheese and celery sticks).

It is not an emperor penguin
a king or queen . . .
Not a prince or princess
a lady or lord . . .
No – just an ordinary penguin
with nest and egg
and Grandma's gammon steak.

Poetry Day

Today's a good day.
Poems everywhere
      peeping
      poking
      running
      jumping
– leaping
from every
           hat
           cat
           rat
           dog
           and
           bus shelter.
There are so many I stumble as I step,
squash them as I walk.
I gather a headful
wondering which to immortalise
for you
in ink
and pen
and A4 sheet . . .
      neatly folded.

*Love from
Pete x*

3

Cat March

He's on my bed
again

                        next to my ear.
He is purring
he is marching –
        left foot up
        right foot down
        left foot down
        right foot up.

I ask my mum why he is marching
and
why he is purring . . .
Mum says it's what cats do.
I ask Mum where
he is going.
She says nowhere
but I know where he is going
                if
        he does not pack it in.

Bully

Harry Pigstore – what a laugh!
Harry Pigstore – in our class.
Harry Pigstore – what a name.
We don't want you in our game.

Harry Pigstore – what a state,
we don't want you for our mate!
Harry Pigstore leave him out,
Harry Pigstore – snout . . . snout . . . snout.

Harry Pigstore – where's your dad?
Drives a Lotus – red Elan,
lead guitar in Roxy Mode,
that big house up Bombay Road!

Got three houses – judo star.
Brother's got a racing car!
Helicopter for your mum.
We're really, really glad
            – you've come!

Stay and play, be our goalie,
Play midfield instead of Coley.
Wanna stay and play tonight?
Stay with us, you'll be all right.

We're your mates.
My name's Russ,
stick around –
be one of us!

Beware of Pets

I like to have a few pets around the house,
but not cats on mats
fish in bowls
dogs in baskets
mice down holes, kind of pets.
No, not that sort . . .
I prefer something more exciting,
life in the wild . . .
bedroom jungle type of thing,
stinging, spitting,
biting, fighting sort of pets.

Polar bears in freezers,
vampires on the stairs,
crocodiles down toilets,
Vulcans on the chairs.
I like piranhas in the bathtub,
cobras in the beds,
pillows full of frog spawn,
spiders with big heads.

My house is so exciting,
a wild world made for play . . .
So why not come and see me?
Yes! Why not come and stay?

Moving Away

My best friend's leaving school
      today,
she's moving somewhere new.
Her house is on the market,
her brother's going too . . .

I saw the lorry loading
      her toys
      her coat
      her hat . . .
      her bike
      and books
      and bedclothes
      her hamster and her cat.

She said –
      she'd come and see me,
I said –
      I'd go and see her,
but I don't like these changes
      I liked things as they were.

Flying Fish

I've never seen a flying fish.
I've seen a load of birds,
swallows, swifts and starlings,
ostriches and cherds . . .

I'm always on the lookout
for fishes in the sky,
a cod fish or a haddock,
a fishcake or a pie . . .

I'd really love to hear one singing
or practising its scales,
pretty little feathers,
pretty little tails.

But
I've never ever seen one
so, please remember me
if you see one
in the bushes
or nesting in a tree.

Love Is

Licks
sniffs
scratches
claws
funny tails
and muddy paws.
Love is having someone
pleased to see you.

Every morning.

Looking for a Friend

I'm looking for a best friend,
someone just like me,
someone good at football,
someone smart and free . . .
I'm seeking someone special
– quite good-looking too –
someone really clever,
someone rich and true . . .

Yes – I'm looking for a new friend
to do the things I like.
    Someone with some money
    someone with a bike,
someone with a pony,
    someone really new . . .
That special kind of person
    that could
    perhaps . . .
        be you?

Spiders

When spiders go to bed
at night
they roll their webs up
nice and tight.
They pop them into little sacks
to carry off upon their backs.

But:
come the morning
(if it's fine)
they hang them out in spider lines
to catch the bugs,
the bees and flies
they need for making
into pies.

Reggie the Roman

'I'd like to be a Roman,'
said Reggie Smith one day –
so he bought himself some sandals
and a flat down Roman Way.
He bought himself a tunic,
a helmet and a spear,
a chariot,
a toga,
and lots of Roman gear.

Reggie felt so special,
as proud as proud can be,
and he even made a banner
(as big as you and me).

You'll see him every morning
strutting down our street
calling 'Hail Caesar!'
to everyone he meets.
He thinks he's really Roman,
he swaggers and he struts,
the neighbours call him 'Regis'
but I call Reggie
'Nuts'.

Tap Dancers

I hear them in the bathroom,
dancing on the taps,
steps as quick as silver,
dresses tinsel-bright.

They live in folds of bathrobes,
they tapstep on their toes,
     Lavender and Lilac,
     sweet Honeysuckle Rose.

They're my secret dancing fairies,
     they flit,
     they fly,
     they float,
wings as frail as porcelain
and tutus white as soap.

Bedtime Prayer

Please –
     help Mummy with her music
     Olly with his sleep
     Daddy with his writing
     and Granny with her feet.

Help soldiers
     nurses
     puppies
all children as they play,

but most of all –
     help Rovers
     beat Spurs
     on Saturday.

Lost Rainbow

One day
coming home from school
(where else?)
I found a rainbow.
Lost
and sad
and torn
and broken
on a garage forecourt.
I picked it up,
wrapped it in a Wonderloaf wrapper
(which was also lost)
and took it home
where I warmed it
and dried it
in front of my mother's fire.
But it died.

I think it must have been
a very old rainbow.

Brett

We go to see our pal most weeks,
we see him quite a lot . . .
and talk to him
and tell him things
and sort of sort things out . . .
        that day we argued in the park
        the day we lost his dog
        the first school camp
        the football cup
        his video
        and games.

We're always talking,
        him and me
        of things we don't forget,
        like being daft
        and having laughs,

        just me
        and Mo
        and Brett.

Love Poem

Iffley church is beautiful
I thought you'd like to know,
walls as old as Normans
who built them long ago.

They built them with their Norman hands,
piles of Norman bricks,
great big Norman ladders,
        shovels
        spades
        and picks.

Yes, Iffley church is beautiful
from tower
        to arch
        and pew
but never in a thousand years
as beautiful

        as you.

Liar

I am a liar
I lie anywhere
and everywhere
all the time . . .

      Couches, carpets,
      seats and floors,
      hotels, motels,
      shops and stores . . .

. . . and once
just once
in a hammock
slung
neatly
      between . . .

JUPITER   AND   MARS

I am a liar.

White Horse (of Uffington)

Who froze your gallop, great white horse
upon the chalkland hill?
Where were you running – running horse –
        why do you lie so still?

Where were you flying – flying horse –
what was the dance you stepped?
Who lay you to the grass
– dear horse –
who stayed
or prayed
or wept?

Where did your partners go
– chalk horse –
when did your music end?
And do you always dance
        alone?
And can I be your friend?

Waiting for my Sister

(A poem about not being collected from school)

I'm standing in the playground
I'm waiting, all alone
my sister isn't coming
and I'm thinking of my home . . .

> I'm standing in the playground
> I'm waiting by the gate
> the teachers are all going
> and it's getting very late.

The playground's nearly empty
there's no one left to play
and I'm getting rather frightened
and I don't know what to say.

> My name is Peter Dixon
> my sister's name is Jean
> I'm nearly
> > nearly
> > crying
'cos I'm only seventeen.

Hospice

Nice word, 'Hospice'.
Sort of tickle-the-lip
make-you-smile
kind of word.

Auntie Win is in a hospice
sleepy head
cosy bed
friends and flowers
comfy hours.

She says it is a happy place.
'Hospice',
sort of tickles the lip.
I expect that's why she smiles a lot.

Shipmate

I saw a sailor stitching
a name upon a sail,
fingers bent and broken,
a needle forged from nail
. . . ten torn shreds of ribbon,
a reel of thin tarred thread,
the words he wove were simple
and the bo'sun bowed his head.
      A ship boy played his whistle
      for a shipmate lost at sea –

gulls laughed in the rigging
and rats danced
fast and free.

Stable

The king – he brought his gift of gold,
a shepherd brought his crook,
the beggar gave his begging bowl,
the leper gave her bell.
A soldier gave his silver sword,
a sad man gave a grin,
the thirsty boy his drinking cup,
a poor girl – just a pin.

The tyrant gave a promise
of peace within his house
       the stable boy brought honey,
         the stable cat –
             a mouse.

Tick

Mum says

Mick

has a tick.

But I can't

hear

anything.

Silly Kitty

Kitty caught a condor,
she pulled it through the door.
I've never seen a condor as big as that before.
It flew around the kitchen,
it ate my granny's hat
and gobbled Father's dinner
and chased away the cat.
It flew into our bedrooms,
it built a great big nest
– on top of Grandma's cupboard
with Father's pants and vests . . .
It laid a clutch of condor eggs,
    it cackled and it shrieked,
    wings as big as bedsheets
– an awful yellow beak!
    The eggs soon split and shattered,
    more condors scrambled out.
    My sister started crying
    and my father gave a shout –
    'Escape!' I heard him yelling
    as we stumbled from our beds,
    condors pecking bottoms
    and flying round our heads!

So now we're in the garden,
we live with birds and flowers.
    The condors live in comfort
    in a house that once –
        was ours.

Christmas Tree

They took me from my winterland
     of frosted rut and thorn,
dressed me in a Jacob-coat
     with baubles bright as corn.

They scorched my roots with sodalime,
they bound my arms with twine,
lights as bright as berries,
candles red as wine.

     Twelve days I dreamed my winterlands,
     twelve days I dreamed my hills.
     dawns of frosted scarlets,
winds and rains, and storms –

Twelve days I wept the forest,
twelve days I dreamed my home,
a forest tree
just winking
of a Christmas –
          all alone.

Bird Table

In order to make our bird table
      a little more interesting
      to summer visitors
we have introduced small chairs,
      napkins
      (folded as swans),
and a complete set of RSPB place mats.

Hopefully:
      the introduction of fly soup,
      casserole of leather jacket,
      and braised carrion
will attract a smarter set of customer

– vultures, penguins,
auks and hawks,
kites and kiwis,
ostrich, stork . . .

We have painted the table
      flamingo pink
and displayed a small sign:

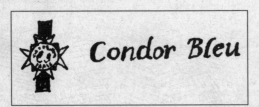

Condor Bleu

Uncle Charlie

I love to lay and listen
when I am snug in bed
to whispers in the curtains,
sounds around my head.

The tip and tap of raindrops,
the grown-ups still up late,
cats and cars and windows,
rattles at the gate.

I love to count the clock ticks,
the hamster's clanky wheel,
my mother checking door locks,
my brother's bass guitar.

I love to lay and listen,
collect the sounds I hear,
and think of Uncle Charlie
who never learnt to hear.

Petland

P is for Petland,
where pets love to go.
The signs in big letters
on the B six nine 0 . . .

You'll see us all going,
wagging our tails,
Scotties from Scotland,
and hamsters from Wales.

It's lovely in Petland,
as brochures all say,
plenty of scratchings
and plenty of play.

There's gnawings and pawings,
cocking of legs,
fighting and biting
and learning to beg.

It's howling in Petland,
it really is fun . . .
snapping and chatting
and smelling our chums.

So: why don't you join us?
Everyone goes . . .
It's easy to get there –
Just follow your nose.